Turn of a Pang

by Nicole Brossard

traduced by Patricia Claxton

Coach House Quebec Translations

Turn of a Pang was first published as *Sold Out* in 1973 by Editions du Jour, 1651 rue Saint-Denis, Montreal.

This translation copyright © 1976, The Coach House Press. Quebec Translations are edited by Barbara Godard and Frank Davey.

Typeset in Stempel Garamond and printed in an edition of 1000 copies at The Coach House Press, 401 (rear) Huron Street, Toronto, Canada M5S 2G5.

The translation and publication of this edition have been assisted by grants from the Canada Council and the Ontario Arts Council.

Pour Stephen

Amicalement

Turn of a Pang

Nicole Brossard

5 mars 1983 - victoria

Things that HIT YOU IN THE EYE with a view to modifying
unconnected clues mobile motives – toward 'latent complicities'
change of attitudes then wonderment.

But the redhead was only the redhead and thence came the difficulty of living the redhead to the full hiding under that head of hair, that sumptuous arrogant mane.

The hidden side.

Radio noises rain down thick in the little kitchen. The tapwater runs a bit too hot not hot enough. The day-to-day gets short shrift in the anonymous adult head bent over the sink, curious and hirsute like a plump fruit hanging over a wall.

The redhead, stepped over carefully in the shag-rugged living room, the redhead at rest, reclining sleeping living stone slowly breathing human stone in that red living room space its occupants some twenty men and women and a few children furtive images of adult faces <u>bathed</u> at this point in sweat smooth water streaming from foreheads from temples down to round soft downy chins in this living room whose atmosphere might recall others but which one remembers most returning to a midsummer quebec night's dream dimly lit and rather erotic when magical thoughts triumphed over those verbal battles busily waged by adults in the adult world here and there time and again in supermarkets ministries and elsewhere too.

The redhead, stepped over carefully ...

Just before, or immediately in the second at hand, a fleeting personal adventure far on the horizon, in the lines of the hand escape and tenderness as in a supreme interpretation of life and death; coming close to past images in a story that wasn't one but in which once deep inside we might expect to find the most transparent clarity

or immediately (sounds of ice in glasses)

Realization of cold in the room the twin of the one next door only a different colour in which a water bed was never anything but a water bed. Stupidly to sleep on.

(ice in glasses)

As for the evening's final words, they mingle strategically with the all-pervading smoke (swallowed held lovingly in the throat).

As regards the redhead, there's only the colour in the glint in my eye in the brightness of my smile cunningly arranging sexes and lips around the silhouettes the time wouldn't survive the excitement would it and

Yes I was dropping softly nicely down

Well traced drawn the line: fingers idly on the dusty glass-topped table in the hall wandering glances right and left, caresses to the cheek another of the major's last goodnights. Balancing over the glass patiently awaiting the distant mirage miracle eyes approaching eyes in the wavy light reflections from the polished surface. Four times the same little wave of the hand and nod of goodbye.

An idea that a redhead (or rusty red the colour of her hair) might be the profile and surface of the story of a text taking us back to the days of wide high heels, of a fashion undebauched except by the wind blowing from behind the Notre Dame Street armament plants. An idea of resemblance with early conscription days, a text that darts here and there weaves the under side of a double-ended reality '41 - '71 (a trail of invisible Ariadne thread leading from one century to another in thirty years of life and privacy in collective isolation in a territory waiting for renewed loves and friendships, backslaps, passionate caresses coursing paroxysms seizing petrified spines of (hunted) wartime lovers, when she wore black (in mourning for her father) svelte and radiant to be hanging on his arm, his young mistress. He (as the picture shows) walks in such a way as to advance gently.

The days of picture postcards in glossy colour, days of cards in pale pastels arriving from Old Orchard. Look closely at this common ground where the romantic come and go of those days perpetuates through the thirty years or thereabouts separating forty-one and nowadays age of biological maturity, orgasm full, fleeting and total in the radiant conscious human animal (quite beyond words but integral in the writing filling space / meandering calligraphy mask of all conceived and stirring in that still firm and tender flesh).

And on the back behind the pink and blue and sea-splash silvery spittle between the rocks, a 3-cent stamp the face of Lincoln cancelled.

a) red, rust: adj. and n.
   'And the little toy soldier is
   red with rust' (Eugene Field)
   'She has the charming mien of
   an adorable redhead' (Apollinaire)
   'Her hair warm and red
   as burnt gold (Villiers)

It stuck (DNA) and one day
reappeared quite unsought in
what the tapping typewriter wrote.

Provocative hue.

Hazy image of that redhead woman reclining on the rug. Not much to note save the all-important colour. Recollection or imagination taking pleasure in reversing the chronological order of events delight in the chase and knowing how it is for my generation born in those times and was for men and women who saw them born. This is not written from memory. Here no personal experience of life as it was in those conscription days. How things looked, shades of rouge and lipstick, the price of cigarettes, the smell of factory smoke, the taste of pale ale, all this is history and comes from books.

Avid stare. Falling snow. Mild fluctuating weather. The line of trees bare fingers clutching at the grey today. Gusting buffeting sulisten and you try with writing to bring forth silhouettes of strange (mythical) specimens of men who come on horseback in bands and leave traces and clues for the eye to grasp ... like an image spreading on the screen when a *Winchester* goes off.

Burst of fine snow blown against the window panes.

And then slipping in with time's passage as wind gusting through cracks between boards comes the moment of truth when man confronts man each to destroy the other. When on the screen closeup comes the man's hat and strains of music yet unheard reach the ear from near from far.

A parody of snow on memory's window pane.

The searching eye.

Eye roving moist glistening system for interpreting the reality in the game of words, complicity of hand and eye induced by the nineteen forties' red mane and wig

(here near the Main in a nightclub not far from the well-known whorehouse at Amherst and Ontario, wigged blondes and red-heads preen for watching eyes in the blur)

red / dyed swirling about itself

The transparency in things opposed to verbal clutter; growing white dot surrounded with rusty red the white spreading lavish covering the red (which fades by degrees as a colour become an obsessional presence / link / all of which belongs already like snow to nostalgia that never drains its source of meaning.

Eye and memory out to lampoon the colour rusty red.

View from across the street. A tram goes by on Bélanger Street. Children wearing great red wax lips. Raspberry flavour. Slow pace of the past cancelling out the effect of anything said that's new and centred on the joy of life. A past relived (so little) imagined with care and philosophic need to understand and want (with a logic other than the logic of those days) the blandishing reality.

An image and at once allusion to that pair of lips locked in wax, whence the silence or (the child's incoherent muttering behind the little crimson mask. Words contained in a game that's worth the candle ... in certain eyes ...

Then there's the memory of after-post-war days (fragmented memory).

Prospects (from palm lines to forehead lines and a few skin folds on a smooth stomach); but then reading the future would make no difference because the terrible lines of fate are hardly drawn in rusty red like a trademark to be read and pronounced properly P E N C I L O knowing beforehand that what's written is offered without guarantee.

Tried oh so hard to reproduce a set of tarots the castles Gleason used to make with cards and that red (briefly visible in the blue geography of the king's jester's habit)

and also the Emerald Tablet whose text he'd retranscribed on China paper or with India ink retraced the golden age of 'that which is above is like to that which is below'.

The redhead seated by his side fine shadows of her hair on the white wall behind. The wax drips (blow the flame black) the light goes out someone IN A CRASH OF GLASS THE CANDLE.

A face with long beard bristling. The ragman sandman in person passing by along the street never does anything worse. July '43 on Garnier Street, crickets chirp. Hoards of children suffocate in the heat (it must be noon) and that one there's an anecdote on all those moving lips, on Garnier Street while a band goes by, coloured form resounding in the wobbly midday air.

An anecdote in the eye.

CHAPTER ONE

Flashback (countdown of years to October 1941 —————— *Citizen Kane* / Loew's 'THE SENSATION OF A NATION' seen and reread behind a memory screen a poster stuck [all those tongues just think] on the movie house wall announcing magically how the verb <u>devour</u> could devour to satiation so much attentive flesh (its surrender when it happens mirror fashion to arouse those gargantuan appetites that a roomful of enthralled spectators in suspension always satisfies).

At every moment (in the queue the spinning) you'd have to expect to see ahead (spidery plot in hot censored climate as lips part looking more and more like vulva to be coloured [wax crayon and contour] as in the image-language children use for secret passages and obsidian lamps) a description of a place and men in broad-brimmed hats and painted ties, feminine mechanisms and procedures said to be oriental once the lipstick colour decoded (recollecting also the scent wafting from the whole mouth whole apple a gleeful comparison [<u>like</u> in a surplus of material]).

Citizen Kane and the same night the El Morocco opening on Mansfield Street 'leading me astray in so many stages on the stools red and resistant to alcohol white and brown, meandering beers and blonde tufts multiplied in my beard oh cunnilingus' the opening and gaping of the El Morocco, the 'oath' circulating among the customers – sharpies and soldiers – under the table nylon frays and bags – curves a word occurring in the time to cross legs —————— cross of thighs under long dress suggesting modesty (Cherry would show up and smile) belatedly indeed for that's done it sweet consuming contact lingering lost in fleshly depths cruel respectful caressing lashes.

Regular perched at the Bar after work. PHOTO, and below the caption, 'Women at work applying airplane fabric ...' Another one, red on her lips, gone on her clientèle, factory rhythmics first on her mind. Weary regular clocked, ready to pass out; heat and mechanics of the gift of life down the drain in wear and tear to the sound of ringing metal and the touch of harsh fabric made for combat of unknown bodies no less eager than the bodies of customers sweating out the dancefloor and torrid October.

Bright-eyed regular conversing the current conversation which means chit-chat about luxuries and when-the-war's-over. Hear the jingle of blackened pennies teeming in drawers which keep away the verdigris from the ennobled face of George VI who struck in copper is a greater threat to peace of mind and body than the censored NEWS at the Granada.

All the streetlamps in the blue-black evenings of July were yellow moons like round moon faces.

Visible (written thus: the body becomes visible through the power of imagery and desire) <u>vivid river moulded in ink</u> (flow as in fauna and flora fl).

Together simultaneously the sense of seeing the visible become an abstraction 'the strangest position in which a mortal could find himself'.

Point of departure inscribed as such in the double play of writing and d-death as *lived* at times of great lucidity, as *prolonged* in the night (sometimes in the afternoon come siesta and solitude) to the sound of heavy trucks passing far away (not very far) while with wide-open eyes one listens to one's palpitating heart, legs apart or together crossed.

The trace   the multiplicity of movements in that time remembered for the ease with which certain caresses grew from the scalp, neck or hip. The preciseness of the moment; the thrust of haunches forcing breath, cutting short its sounds, turning them to enchanted havoc under red-tinted flesh that SHATTERING pulverizing instant.

The single trace in the iris (cat's eye) surprise cleft ... the stomach asserts its presence on the page and to the eye is always magnified by the round-about approach.

A bit of everything in this trumped-up tale of childhood and maturity. Whatever opens the door for acquaintance with times past rich with experience and awareness put to the test by writing that exploits it and compels it to take form.

In rusty red or elsewhere, near factories in Montreal. PRODUCTION.

The formative act that is the sense metamorphosed / metamorphosing (the red of the wig over the black of the pale-face woman's hair).

A trumped-up tale with varied reflections in avalanche (presuming snow) and multiple effects according to the points of view. The instant.

Terrain conducive to dispersion, wandering and rearrangement word for word, for counterbalance precisely as in the word *grace* : 'he with plumed and high-crowned hat who never bears arms but yields them to all comers paler purer white than what's left of the page'.

Encounters seen obliquely or the outline of bodies perceived in the proper way; attracting to oneself the opponent's eye (even using the other's resistance the better to arouse desire) insinuating by that the risk of seeing hazy forms in movement, from that far removed in mirages that are beautiful or cloud one's vision with the extreme terror they inspire

which amplifies everything and deeply disturbs pores and muscles and mind frenzied by encounters seen obliquely.

The anecdote ramifies following recollection's course in the protraction of colours and forms returning to the eye some years later. And in the telling it draws from time past only the fictional necessities. Tells of a presence in an uncertain city (how the expectations lived in it augur the remorse of having lived ridiculously and in the fleeting and also fictional reality of it all at that) passionately the many hours of desire and its dispersion.

Problematics of the colour rusty red reproduced endlessly in red-dyed hair throughout the years (or rather the streets, their historic British names of victory and defeat, their French names from overseas) imitation of excellence, imitation period blustering into place in fictional tongue.

Anecdotic but as briefly as can be in fashioning the event.

The setting and its honourable mentions (Laurentian and Gaspesian zones) in phony storybook development. Rolled virgin parchment of text which exists only for the endless imperative search. An enchanted thought on the occasional occasion of a quebec night beneath the ceiling of pyrotechnics and untwinkling stars.

Fiction admitted to the inner sanctum of symbolic warmth.

The rusty red of bodies male and / or female. Funny how now the text dilutes and is lost in the scarification that adorns an author's stomach. If all hands could touch his stomach together they would read ....
....
....
skin et cætera.

Rusty red / reality: Belmont Park its monstrous folksy dolls laughing their mechanical laugh fit to kill.

Conquest over thought, conquest over yesterday's torment and today's in surges of credulity, and long waits.

Manifestations of intense reflection; signed, delivered (smile) or deep black imagined trace soot signs sequence sz.

Drawer.

Closed: the year 'forty-one, no more barbarous than another, closed again with arms and thighs closed around slim adult bodies silhouettes sculptures. Fiction-actuality of painted lips (Baby we'll paint the town t'night). Lips and thighs open in that little green and grey Ontario Street bedroom. Little panties on the floor, on the devarnished varnish, lacy garter belt (Je vois la vie en rose).

Irresistible urge to sleep and dream (moist cotton-wool sex) vague vagary of a song sung high beneath the weeping willow, foliage above m-me (from that day on she had herself called Cherry).

Cherry dreaming in the rusty red of iodized cotton wool. She worked in Dupuis Frères' basement, in children's underwear. She'd scratched her finger on a rusty nail.

Irresistible urge to waken? Interrogation: tomorrow or tomorrow Sunday or Sunday in three weeks?

Rubis sur l'ongle: pronto, ruby red of finger-nail: Cherry.

EVA / APRIL: thirty-year-old cheesecake pinup whose young body whose yellowed paper remind me of nothing important at all.

Dorchester Boulevard to cross. The time of day when rusty red looks (diffused in the glass of high wide windows) vaguely like a sunset.

Trèfle incarnat their perfume, powdered lipsticked red and white dark-haired daughters of respectable families passing through the revolving doors of the Sun Life the tallest building of all. Nineteen hundred and forty-one in the hand of secretaries employees experts in the fabrication of sumptuous letters opulent in the long sweep of their f's and g's successive curlicews magnificent f's.

SCRIBES

A quebec night (recalled pigheadedly as such to make all seem cheerful almost true by dint of incantation) lived beneath the sky and the chinese red neon lights of Old Montreal. Warm malleable night, plastic as braggadocio would have it. Lurid with luring letters. Circumscribed, hallucinogenic, rhythmed night of soft docile substance on which to lie and not to dream of a world, dense nocturnal halo around the centre of attraction where dying would be other than by chance.

The tourist homes beckon through the dark of this same night. A world apart this quadrilateral [Ste Catherine – St Paul / St Lawrence – St Denis] ! Festivity or conspiracy, a tourist home's just the thing. Room rented for the evening or the night, handily out of reach of the police, finding oneself among friends, talking, smoking, awash with music and rusty red, shadowed jostled by profiles on the white of walls, rooted on the cold oak floor.

Purlieu, tense sequences on display in the Leduc Pharmacy window (24 hours a day / day and night). HArbour, CHerrier, LAfontaine, WAlnut, telephone exchanges knit into one's memory as a single reality. To be dialed to reach a friend when you need one, someone, some stormy night when white spills white, slowly for hours on end.

Snow and sonic background of *Echoes* / *Meddle* / nighttime harmony and more, the ink trajectory, for without that image of sequence and silk, the harmony would seem too uselessly like some figure from the past.

Nineteen hundred and seventy-one an evening in May,pinpointed in time Montreal space and its smell; nineteen hundred and forty-one: baby crying behind the bars of his playpen flowered rubber garden. The world begins with the bursting of shells (oh please not his playpen!). The fabled fictitious quebec night has just begun drags on like waiting in a station.

Drawer.

A network of equivalences to be conquered following the thread of each allusion, each textual membrane (transparent / opaque) formation, disappearance.

'41 – '71 in the rusty red all around the faces that one sees palpable unreasoningly.

A crowd, anonymity. Splendid back ahead, flowing hair; curve of hips or lines of hip moving in tune with that back, be it man or woman, a network of beckoning indicators. To be followed step by step breathing down his / her neck through the labyrinth of English Montreal *how I'd like to follow someone else somewhere else on the black side of this island. The black wave of I happily rendering to pleasure* my French everyday logic stymied, possible sources of fulfilment too.

'I'm coming'
Of everything said that evening, by this extract understand that
the summary of yesterday and today (lifelong presence, courage
always wanting; thus, with the touchof round clear groomed
fingernails 'I'm coming, yes,yes' derisive gaze in the mirror, after,
seeing the effect of that liquid between those legs) predicts the
effect

or rather the sensation it brings lingering in the nerve centres and
other centres of life and pain and tenderness or joy as in that trace
still fresh in the mind's eye drawn by the firm pen nib moving
back and forth writing saying whatever comes / stop:
a WALL around
text ———————————————————— signature
anonymous scribes: ersonal prono.

Skin where hard-line records mnemonic signs of piercing clinches are inscribed as they happen, in my shoulder; as metaphoric as all this world of evidences strung together subway style, underground anyway.

Tactile him of sounds whirling round my ear. Abrasive.

Reverberant in the vast virgin thereabouts pre-November 27, 1943 (the text imagines no more than its experience). Aleph — death and survival through which to reach unobstructed clarity in all this. The plunge. Implant myself in the heart of the impenetrable *point*.

Silence on certain restraints, the ones that so violently fan the urge to follow the phantom trace of meaningless babble, freed of all responsibility, executing the overthrow of destructive occult powers with each voluptuous recognition of the self gripped in a state of ecstasy and execution.

Such as drifting into rapture.

The city and yesteryear have faded now from the paper screen. Cherry the redhead wears herself to a frazzle blinking squinting to see if maybe there's rusty red under the white, watching for subtle shades and effects of forms stirring behind the sorry play of empty space to be filled.

DRAWER

CHAPTER TWO

Any fictional form but factual sequence too. Thus April 22, 1942, five days before the plebiscite, 20,000 *persons* are assembled at the Atwater market. Intrigue is rife. Nothing new but fiction and rattling of bones; chance signs, mysteries, high drama brewed to taste as if to shape a composition from time / on / time holding back the straw that could break the camel's back.

Heads move constantly. The moment is adrift in the folds of cloth coats rubbing together this <u>wartime</u> evening in the unspoken urgency of electing each his special permanent place in the land. Jigging heads (their number creates a <u>state</u> of unsuspected euphoria the very moment of treachery) wartime shell-shaped heads, swellng ears ... jarred by rumbling screeching endless empty Montreal Tramways cars — bane of the French-speaking orators.[1]

Skirmish and ... arms reach out and fall violently on heads ... the sidewalk and horse crap. Ellipse, hustle roughly prodded 'think I passed out getting in the police wagon. I think.' And that's the end of it ... diversion, curiosity, military convoy to be watched parading intestine style or nooselike in the market square .... right beside the police station and the bowling alley. *Men* are recruited there during the little town's descriptive game: situated less than twenty miles from Montreal, the town of Beauharnois boasts two major industries ...

ENTRANCE, a bowling alley and its fury of senseless noise around balls rolling endlessly toward teetering pins. 'There's the soldiers, two cream sodas, Evalinda. Betcha a game it's yer Momo's turn next week'. 'Don't gimme that' pronounced across the countertop. Conversation all around the alleys ... the words crumble: the bowling alley is a huge deserted beach where scenes of reality brew and composites of potential images take form, in infinite variations around the alley and the GRILL an infamous place in Albina's pious old mind out there on the 2nd range just beyond the village; between the alley and the grill the paths are beaten wide 'cause you gotta look like what you are: cattle and beef meat and grill cannon fodder blast between the eyes meat and too much such cannon grill.

EXIT, 'that way if ya finished yer game'. The main street by the park; from there you can see the river and the islands, tranquil nature undisturbed by fishing boats or tankers, islands not far off. Khaki tents in the market square, officers with officious airs barking the word ORDER all over the place 'like goddam loonies'.

Standing and watching the word river, and the islands not far off.

Maurice's truck comes by at last, on the way to Ville Lasalle with tomato plants.

---

[1] On the evening of the protest meeting that took place on February 11, 1942 at the Jean Talon Market, attended by 10,000 people, a constant stream of empty Montreal Tramways steetcars passed not far from the meeting to prevent the speakers from being heard by the crowd.

The redhead sitting on the sofa, arms and hands and fingers cramped, studies an ashtray in front of her, crystal irridescent flower, contemplates the equivalences of colours. Between the eye and the object, a distance travelled at one's risk and peril of surreptitious rumblings foreign to the ear, of the left hand for example moving suddenly. She says, 'I'm not shaking, it's my whole body vibrating'. Excitement fills her with chills with fire, floats her far from reality like seaweed tossed by a frenzied sea like hair of dantesque red (mane-horse-gallop-fury-wild-freedom) necessary process for sustaining unripe images like Gleason's, king of spades with predatory eye, magnificently sodomising the redhead laid on tulip stems on flowered sheet.

Network of thighs about as delicate as muscular projected in the copulatory act, like a twosome of trapeze artists, she writes about the word network so as to give the story continuity. 'Pure madness' — we learn to read together after all — an attempt at corruption, word for word, executed as the occasion arises, hands and fingers skilled in the pleasure of effect confronting the networks (from red to mauve) esoteric ramifications of the lines of the hand, folds that move on the stomach in the languid aftermath, undulatory traces of that same white substance slipping gently toward the permanent reality of death.

Now in 'forty-two all that stood the test of time and orgasm. Such giddy sensations, with in mind the focus contours of a life to live out to its end, kept returning astonishing the character played by a woman of thirty.

Now as then behind the PRODUCTION factories, the men roll themselves a 'good' cigarette, thinking: bam crack oof uh grrr, thoughtfully. Above their heads the letters crowd together caught in a threatening loop. COMIC STRIP.

A celebration of imagery or ... apathy for output and production stirs in their eyes; imagery coloured by thoughts churning in bodies male and female at coffee breaks and the ends of working days, to the shrill tune of the factory whistle spewed above the factory a trace almost locomotive smoka in the wind, longing to get out of there and not come back.

Insistance on electrocuting perforating thoughts of the insane abyss of pleasure. That's what arouses attention: material good for orgiastic consumption (EXCESSIVE USE OF WHAT ONE LIKES) gnawing presence pervading in the neck.

The redhead takes in the presence of sketches and outlines littering the work table. The illusion is perfect; the paper dims, numerical production from zero to vertical one bent in, say, eight other ways so as to proceed with the precise calculation of data which would justify the improvisation.

Self-generated mathematical delirium focus of imagination, of productive effusions also awe-inspiring prospects because I bring them to bear on the ineffable world of conquest.

Fear of looking closely at the one who (as can be seen by looking in the mirror) is engaged in writing. Stare at her face until she notices something and enters bodily into an embarrassing complicity in which seconds are prolonged without one's knowing whether this EVENT satisfies the desire or renews it cumbersome like an unusable weapon.

At this point I should perhaps tell a story of I you he we and other plurals recounting one by one all the phases of the enchantment, reconstructing the play of words and of gestures and their consequences in the quebec microcosm; all the phases in the destruction of the he's and she's, braving each reprieve until the narration finally and surely comes to an end. Time and collective animation, and their recording, pursue their course.

GRAFFITI (plural)   GRAFFITO (sing).

One or other on the rotting wood fence, on the piss-green doors of toilet cubicles.

MANGE D'LA MARDE   Hostie

invocation of excrement, the eating of enigmatic and also representation   and sacraments always

CUL CROSSÉ PAR EN AVANT PAR EN ARRIÈRE
fuck you

to be inscribed out of context on paper when words of that ilk ought to be scratched in hard opaque surfaces so that no one could (or even think they could) extract the letters one by one as if to remove them from decent view, from the obscene hand which might linger caressing the little damp gashes laid bare there for all to see who care

VA CHIER P'TITE PLOTTE A JOHNNY

an invitation to a little slut to go shit. Everyday humdrum overthrowing order and *distinction* established in four walls, and elsewhere than on the wall the handwriting shows in broad slaps of paint across a politicians's mouth

Le QUÉBEC AUX QUÉBECOIS

on his eye TRAÎTRE between his teeth, the phallic Independance I lifting (an impression) the black freshly-daubed moustache.

The crowd because without it nothing is justifiable. Frenzy, confrontation. RESPONSE. Back to square one and all that must go to stem the spate of disharmonys in the age-old habit of writing like we talk.

The crowd (how many are there?) BEFORE always before the something to confront with oneself among others with others before City Hall before parliament or neon Seven Ups or the barricades *yet* .

Text because the references are too easy to manipulate. Places of encounter 'bring on the drinks' ....
....
Something to get across the textual allusions, primary source quotations from line one and face to face defying the phony wooden muscles outstretched brandished here and there and everywhere.

Questions of references: for the moment these those in the mêlée on both sides in the sense that words get to be no more than slogans snarled between teeth, crusted on lips.

The other crowd too that can't get the spirit of the thing without hidden motives of self DISPLAY.

Contrast in a text already running dry through overuse of words responding not with pleasure at all but pigheadedness in willing pleasure 'pretending that the gang's all here so an orgie's in order'. If only once there's no pretense of cause, then *crowd* may be written with reference only to pleasure in the text.

What strikes and unfurls overflows the frightful limit more than the mirror and the second look it makes you take, sight struggle inside the wall reflecting gradually caught in the oval from / what secret? / you see plenty of other things too but that crowds are not all the same no way the same when they're making HISTORY (hieroglyphics on what surface when you think of it? — to be decided as events unfold [there must be surfaces as much as compasses for scratching them]).

Crowd / surface there crowds submerge, or a symbolic number descends toward — —

Even if only an illusion, being inscribed here in such an imperfect place as euphoria in textual form if one is willing to add a bit of what is said transcribed transformed thus the word crowd couched hovering in the horizontal version of the atmosphere that emanates on nights of mass meetings / you meet all kinds at times like that.

The pattern the die elbow to elbow. Sure enough 'something' is worn away from the originality roars horribly in the atmosphere, faces transform magma 'I think nothing but fire these days' EXIT.

RED-EXIT cardinal points sentinels.

The impression rather than the true image of ... then suddenly (the place the Forum, pop show) hands above supplicating heads toward *le* stage HOSTIE!

LE STAGE HOSTIE expression imposed by the cultural context as initial reflex. Stage floor, smooth surface, guidemarks to move along / oh how we'd like to see the star mated with another star during the SHOW ... the sounds come in separate rooms around the ears of each receiving singular lapping up the crowd sound. We imagine we're at the Forum in the valley, the pit, the rink. And places of fire begin all over piercing to confuse the blackness. Multiple fires held at arm's length.

Absolutely describable; the thirsty paper drinks black soaks up fluid and germinates letters (splash) word for word I we back to the start of the text recounting with absolute authority the years lived from 1941 to '71.

Delve into, drain the pleasure at its most intense the deafening image and the very essence of a show's appeal.

Reference: understand that *wave* at the source of what is signified 'I'm quite old enough to touch another woman' reference to the mirror, episode of 'never felt anything so soft'.

Crowd multiplication of senses approaching sign IN.
                                            a leg caressed while he lights
                                            a cigarette.

Amplified sound of senses adapting to the cold fire of noise collective apprenticeship in the search for crowd pleasure effects.

A question arising when touching on multiplicity. The number among the staggering number of beings outlined on the retina, sometimes separate, almost always lost in the reality of Montrealers pouring their doubles one by one on *the mimicking surface of the mirror paper,* taking all of them in at a glance and in prose made of resistance and abandon.

Because wanting one thing means unconditionally sensing the reality of its opposite, and by that very fact formulating an impossible concordance of language to fit what has to emerge as some instance of pleasure.

Overlapping factors: restlessness in the line of crowding mass sombre point because of number.

Sombre point identified: enveloping stirring blotch darkness lingering there at length barely moving impregnating space with flux.

From sombre to rusty red turning back to an exploration of particular acts: play of anecdotes the better to pinpoint the environment words and entire passages spawned; they'd be written reproducing in their rhythm the slow calligraphic movements that go with their inscription.

CHAPTER THREE

Bluff, starting with that like the eery whistle of a 22 slug amid the buzz at the cheerful friendly 'barbotte' on Papineau Street. Bluff oozing like pus from the whole room, wounds in necks; vampires on the prowl watching the colour of the folding money and the shiny coins strewn on the table, on the green felt (a green that bathes the eye succulent seductive shadow, *meadow* green crowning the array of colours or flowers of the fields; green of a sudden soothing or ominous ['what if I go home stark naked']) around it players smile and brood in the anonymity and majestic arrogance of clandestinity.

A glance then play. Cards knaves queens red or losers reappraised in a language of the people but foreign to the custom whereby in order to communicate one has to talk like everybody else. Surface atmosphere   dream   like Rodolphe's imagining his victory over Edmond after five years of weekly defeat.

Small room; today it's the kitchen. Yesterday the 'dicks' padlocked the bedroom door. 'They tip us off anytime they're gonna raid'.

Léo loses, loses, wins then asks for more chips and puts them by the sink. White and soft clunk of wooden chip. Hot coffee, gros gin spilled on the felt cloth, between brown suspenders and on Pierre's white shirt.

A private place familiar to initiates, on the inside shiny like a new vinyl floor. Trademarks on the walls; Black Horse and calendar, crucifix; smell of cigars, half-eaten apple on the corner of table no. 6, description without solution of the dream world fashioned from the other world, the real one, where one wouldn't dream of invading a woman's bingo game with its stale nostalgic air 'might as well pass the time while we wait'.

Poker face and agile fingers. Always the fear of the classic cardshark (silent stranger, tatooed, shifty-eyed) pure invention made of adjectives and coincidence. A preserved specimen image poking through the screen on which the line of chance is already traced with its Straights and Royal Flushes winning species in hard cash.

Outside the 'barbotte' two Quacks pass hips swinging under their unbecoming uniforms, already weighing their words before reporting to the lecherous Captain Larouche of the Van Doos.

Today as it happens, having contemplated the crowd the redhead is considering returning to the private place that gratifies her so. An ambiance propitious to desire and its corridors of fantasy. Imagining with eye and hand and a dreadful urge to brave all, to lose herself there (inside her the provocative *germ* of near-frenzy, of dangerous liasons). To be perilously at the brink of. Ravaging the page with herself, reflecting that temptation is an open door to all sensations of fulfillment.

Manifestation of south-shore suburban transgression in Brossard – version told at the provincial Police Station; Cherry surmises that this time silence won't get her out of the fix she's in. Words: say all, tell all, reveal all 'til they're saturated hearing <u>stories of</u> <u>blow jobs, sodomy,</u> kinky whippings over tender young <u>backs</u> ... in lady-like terms ... like <u>poor tired little penis.</u>

Transgression in words how and once it's written what is it if not violence by the writer exploring, if not violence by whatever stands in the way of conquest, of domination over the self, and over others I'll be told.

It might be written too that to tell the truth Cherry wasn't really involved just visiting in that little suburban town lit like a tombstone.

Rain, a mirror in each puddle.

Dreams and drawers closed again. Watchful-waitress EYE.

Scars / tattoos, something not unlike writing being traces and effect of language in the skin through play of dotted lines or incision by metal in the flesh (Hawaiian dancer, arrow-pierced heart or cobra) bare chest, belted corpulent waist, St Lawrence Main, picture-plastered shop; 'Special price to musclemen'. POSTER. 'If it hurts smoke a joint'. 'You got a fine body bejesus'.

CLOSED: the tattooer's tattooing the too fat cat the big shot of the Main.

Scene unchanged the quadrilateral (streets) *yellow circle* on the map *misshapen eye* — criss-cross of fuzzy lines: Montreal — thousands joined by telephone lines (the network); absolute space reduced to a telephone book a little organism feeding the city with its coded symbols.

Word association, password combination set hard in the memory, beautiful symbols. Parallels/perpendiculars coming into focus with concentrated looking at the yellow, the circle, the precise location looked for.

Exemplary rusty red target of a watery barrage from the sky ('mobile walls of rain' I'll soon be thinking). Hair (each strand, its role in the structure of the whole only too alive moving in caressing hands as to chords of Latin-American music syncopated breathless uh-uh; plexus [interlacing vessels, journey]) hallucin .... channel of lifeblood and a vague wave, the journey of novelistic fiction in the human body, Saturn rings turning BLACKOUT the network once again blood vessels clear red or rusty, spacelike.

Alcohol (St Catherine Street) noises, a smell of Acapulco Gold.

Every alcohol-infiltrated vein burning impurities, burning the inner body, consuming it like incense watched by the strange eye of the kingfisher or could it be a decorative Season's Greetings on the wall that catches and provokes the eye, brilliant red and evergreen boughs. White; the alcohol pervades, reaches the broad spaces inside, nautical and fabulous.

Nineteen hundred and forty-one and remembrance of a text destined to mark a two-fold temporal reality before and now in the familiar but also unsuspected Montreal of conscription days.

For an ABC of a certain collective life in the city as lived at the time but to emerge later and elsewhere in a sense full of purpose. Here however there'll be no talk except to consider two *proper* nouns (Cherry and Gleason) and a few **common** nouns names of streets and public places.

The etc. of thought in a difficult text, *terrifying* urges to harp on the *long legs of desire* pure fiction of ordinary words absorbing more than the hypnotic pendulum.

Space; decorative alphabct crowning west-end department stores.

Sliding doors, open windows at spring-cleaning time, space, the city, the *tentacular* metropolis as in a book on American architecture which if paid more attention to would sow panic *inside* a body spent / spending its reserves of energy bit by bit.

....

Lugubrious rings lycanthropic eyes above the city. Aggression as in a bad dream in which Cherry could lose life the ultimate right majestically with her whole body to love the mask and velvet pelt of the wolf-man devouring (figures of speech) with his eyes the hot-dog eaters issuing contentedly from the A&W.

Probe with infinite care the meaning of the various airs she puts on daily playing the continuing role of <u>correspondent.</u>

Mail-text-form to fill out. Spinning letters inscribed; invade the fictional almanac and <u>attack the nitty-gritty the subject,</u> positive pickup (<u>comparison with</u>) the needle on the black plastic surface of the disk. STYLUS.

Proliferation of India inks in signals — multiplicity of scattered lines rearranged — suddenly, which form a mass of senses, an agglomeration of infinite beauties (bird's eye view of) canvas and patch of stimulus gradually transforming the viewer's eager eye into an artist's.

Punctuation nil, initial reflex ... followed by an express and formulated urge to prepare the ground for exploratory plays.

Plan for one like any profound intense sleep; dark trace of words inward curve to the rosy channel of cerebral circumvolutions.

Flooded with non-visual images, images running <u>phenomenally</u> wanton on the scalp, differentiated from retinal intuitions, from the moisture that turns them to a carnival of uncertain hues.

... from delights new-discovered linking I and we to the vulnerability of one's temples.

Use of symbols, the ones above the letters (on a typewriter keyboard) slipped into the spaces between the words.

Composition become space and silence between the sounds of words, knocking reality from its pedestal (image of smooth plexiglass and fibre binding or is it the eye caressing the FIBRE (material) that binds d (fib) Konstruktion.

Space-word: interval prolonged 'til all resistance fades so the thought advances, 'so' that makes the tacit link, if one likes, to something luminously obvious in the precise order of juxtaposition of obvious pleasures to which no character in 1941 or today or any fictitious person could HOLD A CANDLE 'when I give it the works'.

CHAPTER FOUR

Incitement to follow the flow, the bustle of people going somewhere or just walking in Phillips Square. A simple circulatory movement, and the starchy circumference of department stores catches the easily-influenced eye on this the evening of the Proclamation of the War Measures Act. 'Some people say ...' – 'What d'you expect, we're at war'.

On their delivery route, a milkman's horse is racing an iceman's. The streets are wide, giving rein to imagination and chalk graffiti. 'Pierre love Pierre' like a monstrous piece of gossip. Private Lebrun gives voice to a plaintive ballad in the corner restaurant while Ginette, who instals fabric on the frames of aeroplances, counts her savings and thinks over the proposal she's had from the little blond St Denis Street boy. Goose pimples, restless epidermis, 'so what? Oughtta get married though ...hope there's some wedding rings left at the jeweller's'.

In front of the Chénier monument a bum bundled up like a polar bear, scarf flapping, sounds off interminably at the red maple autumnal beside him, its leaves not falling fast enough to suit him and his mind-boggling drinker's tempo. Since the world began the old souse Charland has come to sit every evening by the monument, gazing at it with haggard face as though it were Chénier himself or perhaps the English still come bursting all too violently into his memory.

From behind his hornrimmed glasses Charland studies the situation; the monument, the bridge not far off, the neighbourhood children. He rails for nothing, with a stray dog there in front of him eating a dry hotdog off the endless curb.

Buildings, streets, things, all seem perpendicular to one another. A vast array of little crosses seen from a window from which someone is leaning now, against the ledge of weathered cement soiled white by carrier pigeons which sooner or later will take off for Halifax and elsewhere on their way to the far-flung beaches of Normandy with their deserted casinos.

Text and memory, book-ends on the mantle-piece in a Craig Street shop window. *Junk* invades the eye, junk, perchance to buy if the owner doesn't overdo either his praise of the junk or his price.

Bustle, clattering tramcars; a jelly bean deep in his pocket, Charland teeters.

Word for word within the plot, the narration of whose principal events take place in Montreal at two precise points in time with lapses of silence inside the compact mass of **black** thoughts (IN PRINT).

PLEA BY THE EYE [I] FROM A SENSE FOR SENSE
TO WHAT IS GOING ON IN CERTAIN SUR-
ROUNDINGS CENTRE OF ATTRACTION OF
LUCID SKIN [IF THAT IS, THEN WHAT IS TO
COME HAS ALREADY BEEN WRITTEN / READ].

All things that return to mind are muted in the daily figuration of calligraphic back-and-forth in which a line seething with bits of sentences BEHIND THE NOTRE DAME STREET FACTORIES confuses the eye so thoroughly one really can't be sure what form what character one has settled on to impart it all.

From incitement [eye-opening] to informing by the expedient of writing in perfectly natural train of thought informing DIFFERENTLY dropping *loose* gratuitous signs of sense and possibility.

'O.K. so we're tough you 'n' me, but that there stiff last night, who wuz it?' as in narration built of juxtapositions, with emphasis mostly on the juxtaposition and always following the *trace* and catching the eye by jiggling a few vandalous phrases of oblique significance as in something crossed out.

Stupefaction: watching numbed by a kind of nerve centre inhibition, the images heeded so little, measured so little to one's heartbeat, that around the self, in the language chosen, colours and words come crowding which don't go together but once they're put together complete each other perfectly, sodomites, inFORMing bodies, imprinting them horizontally in the moul ... the bodies fall thick and beautiful to the tune of the typewriter tapping (accents acúte and circumflêx).

Fade in on hair (the word) on the surface / if the sense could designate a geography in the mute lines of the orb of the eye, blues, reds, veinlike traces, then (marks the continuity) ... / shining oily / but if rusty red becomes something other than hair HOW is the metamorphosis to be interrupted and the wave furrowing one's forehead checked, there above the eyebrow drawn like an anomaly inside a wrinkle.

(Pron. / auxilliary) walks the city trying to keep silent between Delormier and the Main (from north to south, parallels don't mean nearly as much). People-cages and metaphors abound (tourists gape, swallowing flies and antiquated old world French terms 'le kartier fransay oh yeah!'

Long march on Montreal by a determined walker beaten (through huffs and puffs his stumbling bilingualism explained: the gorgon, multiple tongues in her hair moving / touching if you consider the light in those eyes beneath the waving hair) THUNDERING ONOMATOPAEIAS (Plessis Street) seven *Cobras* roar by, asses tight on the seats of their bikes.

Elements of the EVENT: establish a relationship between Cherry, the amount of dye in her hair, Gleason's virility, also of course (nineteen hundred and forty-one) as isolated (point of) reference (point) on the phallic I in graffiti … childish scrawls inventing a new game of exploration with clues to follow (?!:$). Trails and clues indelible in the memory lead to the scrapheap behind the 'blasted' factory belching black smoke. Remembering this recitation:

'Consentez-vous à libérer le gouver
ement de toute obligation résultant d'engagements antérieurs restraignant les méthodes de mobilisation pour le service militaire? (27 avril, 1942)'.

Surface and transparency: objects under glass (doll, perfume [bottle of], pen, key-ring, necklace) to be lifted with aluminum tongs hanging from a chain. *A dime, a flop, another dime, another flop*.

Sunday, yesterday afternoon, it must have been about five o'clock; a fanciful jumble of intentions and come and go (after the dime machine bit) all about a word (penis) in the mouth.

Illustration streaked all over the surface of play and over most of the images in this calligraphic assemblage. Pauses: man in the crowd, kneeling woman (fellatio) and other many other amorous poses / PAUSES extirpated from daily life in order to know their pangs (quickened heartbeat, rush of blood through delicate tissues and membranes) the delicious consequence.

An inner current, a circulating image, oblique words that tell of it and intrude on the body of the image soon confounding it with the atmosphere it exudes. Shadows swell, their breathing unseen by the eye but perceived, a bewildering encounter between two subepidermal mysteries (far beyond the reality of language).

....

epidermis and camouflage ('you wouldn't know her') a perfect ruse for Gleason who dares not touch and recognize.

And then he finds himself on the brink of tears.

It's here the knavery begins, words slipped in by stealth by the anonymous but potent presence that always imposes its own translation *poetic remembrance* in italics; there is a potency in the art of camouflage. The sovereign eye knows where to find the crack the weak point and make it the hub of ludic anarchy – such literary artistry.

CHAPTER FIVE

The façade of Windsor Station is quite old. The porters in blue are black; the people giving tips are white, conscripts and volunteers, and leaving for Halifax. Trains arrive and depart. Ginette has come to meet Pierre of St Denis Street. Tales of daring, fictional and in the cards. Jules Verne / Walter Mitty on the station platform. 'I saw him I tell you. Look, it IS Edmond.' Fantasy and portions of truth. Loudspeakers broadcast English sounds that metamorphose, by chance as Pierre of St Denis Street sets his foot on the second step of the railway car, into Lili, preying mantis, Dietrich, Marlene nectar gathering among the many sexes male and virgin. Warm soft female balm 'What more can a guy want!'

Here we see mere episodes of impersonal allegiance to the Prime Minister's decree advancing toward the railway cars, looking for a window seat the better to wave (biting their lips) to those staying behind to work and make babies.

The ring of iron-clad heels on terrazzo the chequerboard station concourse, elbow-jabs handshakes and kisses. **The ring of iron-clad heels on the chequerboard** advance and capture, losers win; officers stop and pose in front of their railway car for a picture. Front page of The Gazette, first edition: SEVEN OFFICERS KILLED BY LUNATIC; picture, corpses, chortling brooks of blood. Inset left corner, face of the suspect, the maniac assumed to be the perpetrator of the crime, an east-end wino 'one of those French Canadians who live like animals near the bridge'.

Above the crowd of soldiers' relatives and friends the station clock shows its hands; killing time, Edmond studies it as if it were a race sheet showing, in order of calculated chances of victory, the names of horses running at the Aqualiente track in Mexico over the next three weeks.[1]

[1] During the war, all American racetracks were closed and Montreal's (clandestine) gamblers resigned themselves perforce to betting on horses running in Mexico. Race results took four hours to arrive.

So rusty red inscribes hair and dye and grotesque too in the text and the past. Handled (like plasticene) and written (laid on a surface) rusty red that ought to arouse manifold interpretations and offers perhaps just one; but when repeated, should it be singular or plural ....
when you *think* about it (hanging on the thread of the story, like a sleepy spider) ...

A circumscribed zone containing linguistic deviations and intentions to put words on paper; circumscribed, to be described, placed before the reading eye; its dimensions and possibilities for interplay of (inexhaustible) meanings. ZONE; place of betwixt and between, between the brief yes and no shorn of all tone, hence zone place of atmosphere open to any interpretation or intervention.

Traced (signed) on the surface, a graphic approximation of thoughts receding and returning. Being such (thoughts): short circuit / flash; (insane) almost hazardous demonstration.

Very breathless and very redhead in the taxi taking her from downtown (west) to St André Street (room to rent) in the back seat, very irked by the driver's leer in the rearview mirror 'Cigarette?'. The leather sticks to her thighs and holds them down, activates, slowly dampens her pants. Very enravished, lounging on the moleskin (having come) relaxed spinning out the sweetness of it with reiteration of the definition: 'long combing wave produced in certain estuaries by the meeting of ebb and flow'. Tidal bore.

To sow *trouble* taken literally: plan embodying personal risk (smile and snarl each in turn exorcising the other / important signs ramified proceeding toward the buccal exit / spoken signals) confounded by all that daily practice in hatching (TROUBLE MAKER) effects with words.

Forthcoming in the trouble-sowing play, transparent three-dimensional alphabets; equivocal at the very least.

Bloody Mary the red sticks on the retina. MANIFESTO. It adds I have the impression that 'my inspiration is afloat somewhere in the room'. Music brought that on yet I quote from source, departing somewhat from the text to be sure.

Paragraph.

Vulva and glans emerging in the light. On the retina.

Cartridge: 'place the cartridge either end first in the body of the pen.' Accessory essential to the continuation of the event the flow of intertwining lines, POX on the click or rather the requisite resolve as though luxuriating and infuriating went together, ensued without conjunction in one's mind and ran together outside the text   marginal gripping too much in the thoracic cage, that void of inspiration spent.

Spotlight on the initial rusty red. Next page.

Resistance of the ground against her flat mat back on the sands of Oka by the lake by its glare of blue against its cloudless double.

A bottle of Black Horse on the shore, incongruous with the sand and lapping water ... at the hour when sailboats drop their sails and glide toward the forest edge and evergreen boughs (in Cherry's armpits humidity and scent of wood) ....
.... on the road a few miles later, through squinting half-closed eyes open country and a few wide-brimmed hats sighted near St Eustache. Safety catch. Someone must have fired; 'Came from there for sure. Of course, it's the season'. AUTUMN.

Put boat and oar in the calligraphic bl to let what's waiting there beneath the skin fill and be filled before luninating the words and surfaces we happen to offer smooth burnished smoother still (hot wet palm) the snare of dual appearance / appurtenance of textures (canvas for example).

Calling up the past indeed by examining the ecchymosis, bl skin turned blue more precisely like the violets in Purple Garden (neon).

Diagonal / a slice of yesterday's everyday life (classified relics) DOWNTOWN parallel strings of onions, US.

A twist of <u>tell me a story of rusty red</u> in a maze of clever expressions 'I get an eyeful' whenever I read or after anyway.

Blank space.

Sunday singular somnolent day. Picture image and violence curve of neck picture of singular desire (rape), of coarse hand on that graceful if slightly grubby neck.

Laid out full length of the word body on a surface tender spring grass Cherry poses and click COVER girl on all the newsstands to be viewed with jaundiced eye rusty red by passers-by and foxy exiles in Greater Montreal.

Rusty red imbibed as in blotting paper and rough texture in the porous textual material, by that insinuating that any bookish demonstration infiltrates the immediate entourage of more or less anonymous exposures 'portrait of a redhead at suppertime' imagination drifting off occasionally in midstream to light on something else, long enough for an excuse to be alone.

Here rests the scrutinizing eye.

Persistent pangs the breast their source and target (an avalanche but off a duck's back), well and truly parenthetic in the weft (the goal and pleasure) of interwoven words.

Pangs to see it all pour out pouring sp-sperm begging to be spoken.

Redhead Cherry in name alone, the lexicon of rusty red simply must be made (small personal adventure; sequential peradventure).

Let EAST (direction) be taken as a manifestation of a CULTURAL offense (sequelae, sequelae ...). WE anonymous pops up anyway as part of a play of characters. TYPESETTER: 'It's Friday and we got Monday off'.

Competition from space little black book and telephone. For her finger enters each little plastic circle and touches the three letters and the digit printed in black, works best that way. She dials (composes) it's visible the number in her head. The code and its evolution; the network ... at the other end of the WIRE yakkity-yak comunication.

Acts and cultural acts and animal cheery old imaginary legendary bestiary and subliminal cyclic carrousel of colours at the Faisan Doré something's left from 'forty-three seen with half-closed eye then wide open minutes later he perceives himself in the barroom mirror white like a gravesheet perceives it was first rusty red he'd seen then heard the conscript's voice.